Chas Addams

NIGHTCRAWLERS

SIMON AND SCHUSTER, NEW YORK, 1957

Of the 91 drawings in this book, the 53 appearing on the following pages appeared originally in *The New Yorker* and were copyrighted in the respective years shown by The New Yorker Magazine, Inc.:

PAGES 37, 83, 92 top (1954); PAGES 8, 9, 13, 17, 19, 28, 34, 39, 56, 61, 69, 77, 81, 85 (1955); PAGES 7, 11, 23 top, 25, 27, 35, 42, 48-9, 51, 53, 55, 57, 65, 67, 71, 73, 74, 96 (1956); PAGES 10, 15, 16, 21, 22-3, 30, 33, 38, 45, 47, 52, 63, 75, 79, 87, 89, front endpaper, back endpaper (1957).

The remaining drawings appeared in newspapers as a McClure Syndicate feature.

FOURTH PRINTING

LIBRARY OF CONGRESS CATALOG CARD NUMBER: 57-12399
MANUFACTURED IN THE UNITED STATES OF AMERICA
LITHOGRAPHED AND BOUND BY RAND McNALLY & COMPANY, CHICAGO, ILL.

Publishers' Foreword

Here is Charles Addams' NIGHTCRAWLERS.

Other Charles Addams classics are:

DRAWN AND QUARTERED

ADDAMS AND EVIL

MONSTER RALLY

HOMEBODIES

Which is enough publishers' foreword for anybody.

THE PUBLISHERS

"Well, Kendrick, still think I'm just an alarmist?"

"*. . . and now, George Pembrook, here is the wife you haven't seen in eighteen years!*"

"We won't be late, Miss Weems. Get the children to bed around eight, and keep your back to the wall at all times."

"Same time tomorrow, then, Miss Straley?"

"Better let him play through, Hartley."

"For goodness' sake, stop that chattering and let your father think."

"I suppose I owe you a word of explanation. Less than ten seconds ago I was dropping a coin in a wishing well up in North Wilbraham, Massachusetts."

"We could never have done it without him."

21

1

2

WARNING

THROWING SWEEPINGS
CONTAINING NAPHTHA-
LENE, CAMPHOR BALLS OR
FLOOR SCRAPINGS, OIL
SOAKED RAGS, EMPTY
PAINT CANS, OR ANY OTHER
INFLAMMABLE OR COM-
BUSTIBLE SUBSTANCE IN
THE INCINERATOR IS UN-
LAWFUL AND SUBJECTS THE
OFFENDER TO A PENALTY.

"... and don't think I don't know you're lying there wishing you were with
someone else."

"Seems like an awful lot of cellar for a one-family house."

"Ask him how long we'll be stuck here. This damn thing's timed to go off at exactly 5:30."

"Mmmmm—smells good, dear. Who is it?"

"The way I look at it, if we don't do it, someone else will."

"*Please come right in, Mr. Mallory, and congratulations on a hair-raising yarn.*"

"*YOU WOULDN'T DARE . . . you wouldn't dare . . . you wouldn't dare . . .*"

"Heights make him dizzy—now he tells us!"

38

"Yes, it has great charm. I can't imagine why they want to sell."

"Careful of poison ivy, Lois."

"You're right. It _is_ still wet."

"*Holy smoke! Have you guys seen this script?*"

1

2

5

6

3

4

7

8

"No, I don't know of any children's camp around here. Why?"

"A man has to eat."

"Can't you get along with __anybody__?"

"You're right. That's exactly what they look like."

"It isn't that amazing. Of course he put it in there while it was still an egg."

"Number 468 . . . a slave."

"Looks like Wesselman's hit on something interesting."

"By George, you're right! I *thought* there was something familiar about it."

"Something . . . inexpensive . . . for a . . . scientist."

"Now remember. No spectaculars."

"It should remedy not only your dead area difficulties but also compensate for frequency drift and spectrum modulation."

"I think I've just about got my mole problem licked."

"So far, so good. You took the flour and milk, and added the sugar, the baking powder, and the vanilla. You folded in the egg whites. _Then_ what did you do?"

"Oh, for Heaven's sake, Dudley, why not give him the raise and be done with it?"

"Where have <u>you</u> been until this hour of the morning?"

"I'll say this for John Ringling North—he doesn't give up easily."

"*Well, young man, it's all set. You will graduate magna cum laude this Wednesday, and next Monday you start as copy chief at B.B.D. & O.*"

"We're out of dwarf's hair, dearie. Can we substitute?"

"*Someday, son, this will all be yours.*"

"I told you you'd have to rough it, Isabel."

"This isn't going to be as tough as we figured."

"I hope you're not angry, Ed. I just _had_ to see you."

"Before you let yourself get carried away with all this, Ethel, let's find out if we can list it as capital gains."

"It does give him a certain incentive."

"Just a minute, you guys—we're missing one shovel."

"I'll bet he wants to borrow something."

"Does it occur to you, Agatha, that this is hardly the occasion to use an
expression like 'knee-high to a grasshopper'?"

"... and it goes on to say that 'measures are under consideration to stop the growing nuisance of Peeping Toms, although it is felt that, by and large, they are a harmless group of ...'"

"Just back up a little, dear, so you won't cut my head off."

"*Of course, my parents were furious when I married outside my religion.*"

"...yes, Virginia, there _is_ a bogeyman."